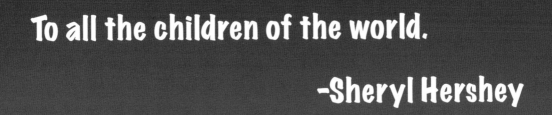

To all the children of the world.

-Sheryl Hershey

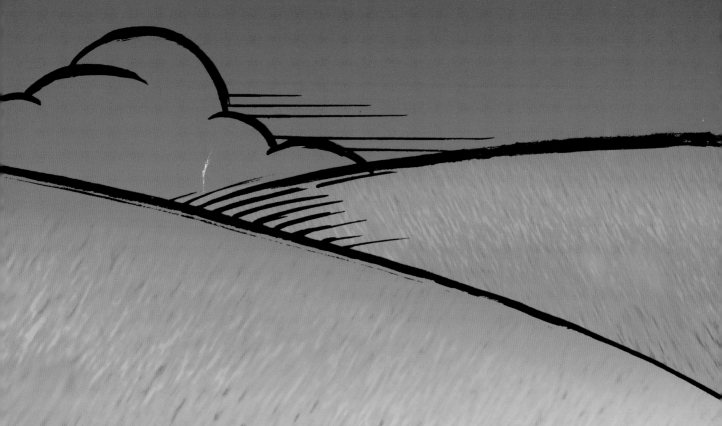

Lila and the Dandelion

Sheryl Hershey

Illustrations by
Michael James Marshall

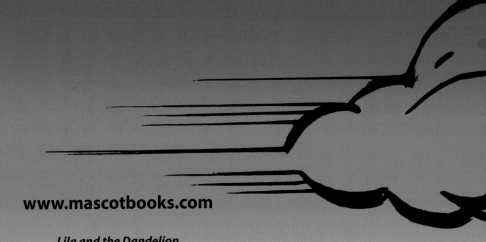

www.mascotbooks.com

For more information, please contact:

Mascot Books
560 Herndon Parkway #120
Herndon, VA 20170
info@mascotbooks.com

Library of Congress Control Number: 2014917080

CPSIA Code: PRT1114A
ISBN-13: 978-1-62086-956-7

Printed in the United States

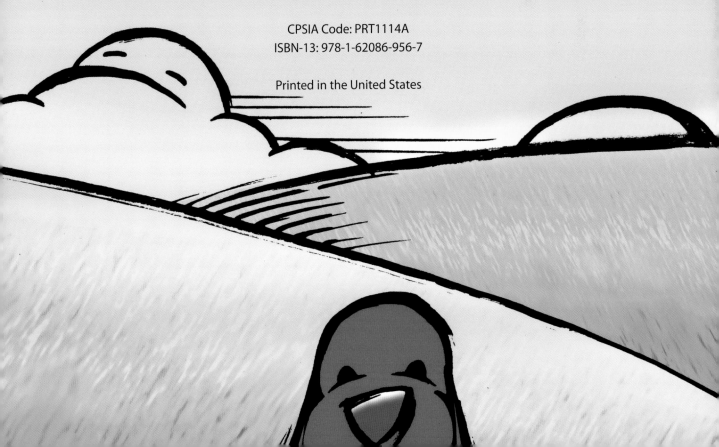

Lila is a **happy** girl.

She **loves** animals, flowers, and **playing** in the sunshine.

Lila does not **hear** with her ears like most children.

Instead, Lila **listens** with her heart and **speaks** with her **hands**.

One day, as Lila was **walking** with her **friends,**
she **sensed** a small cry
coming from a nearby field.

She looked and **looked,**
but couldn't see who was crying.

As Lila walked into the field, she **saw** a sad, little, yellow flower.

The little flower was **crying**.

Nobody plants me in their gardens.

When I get lonely, I creep over to the garden and **pretend** I am a flower so I can have **friends.**"

The flowers must **love** having you there. Maybe that's why they sing so much!"

"No," said the dandelion.

"The gardener **pulls** me away from the flowers and says,

'**Go away!** You're a weed!'"

"Well, Dandelion, I do not think you are a weed," said Lila. "You are **bright, beautiful,** and **look** like a **flower.**

Dandelions are **used** for **food.** They are used for **medicine** to help children who are sick. Even bugs **like** dandelions, and that helps the other flowers!"

The little dandelion felt **happier** now.

He **realized** that it was **important** for him to be **exactly** who he was –

a **beautiful, helpful** dandelion.

Lila was also **very happy.**

She knew that every **living** thing had a **purpose.**

She and Dandelion didn't have to be perfect to make the world a **better** place.

It was better just **because they were** in it.

This is how **Lila** and **Dandelion** became **friends.**

Together, they would **make** the world a **better** place.

The End

Mrs. Lila Ahlsten was a dedicated teacher of deaf/blind and multi-disabled children many years ago at the Washington State School for the Blind. She was a very special person that worked with many children that experienced numerous disabilities due to the rubella-measles epidemic. These children required very special teachers who were dedicated and saw the ability in many who were so disabled. Mrs. Ahlsten was this type of person and believed in every child with whom she had the privilege to serve. *Lila and the Dandelion* is a testament to not only Mrs. Ahlsten, but all people that see the ability in each and every child.

-Superintendent, Washington State School for the Blind
Dean Stenehjem

Lila and the Dandelion was written as a tribute to my grandmother, Lila Ahlsten, who spent her life teaching children who were blind, deaf, and couldn't speak. The illustrations of Lila in this book were made to look like my granddaughter, Skylar, who would have loved the real Lila if she had known her. My hope is that this book will help children understand, in a fun and whimsical way, that they don't have to be perfect to be important in this world.

-Sheryl Hershey

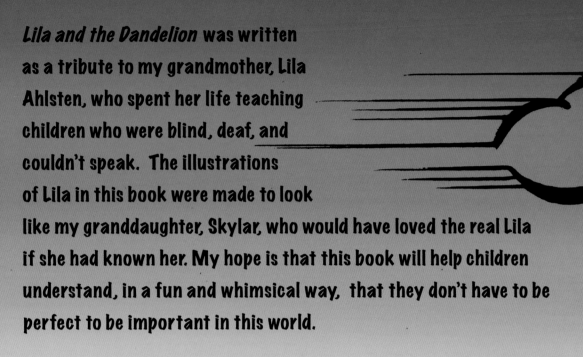

Children's books give parents a wonderful opportunity to learn how their child sees the world. If you and your child have read Lila and the Dandelion, here are a few sample questions that you may use as you embark on a delightful conversation with your child.

1. Lila talks with her hands. If you could talk with your hands, tell me how you would say:
   a) Happy
   b) Sad
   c) Dog
   d) Excited
   e) Sunshine

2. What animals are in Lila and the Dandelion?

3. If you could be friends with one of the animals in the book, which one would you choose? What things would you and your friend do together?

4. Lila says that the world is a better place because you're in it. What is your favorite thing about you? How does that make the world a better place?

5. Think of someone who is special to you. How does that person make the world a better place?

6. There are many colors in this book. Show me where you see:

Blue

Green

Yellow

Pink

Red

7. Do you have a favorite color? What do you like about that color?

8. Lila doesn't hear anything with her ears because she is deaf. What does it mean to be deaf? What do you think it would be like to not hear anything?

9. When Lila meets Dandelion, Dandelion is very sad. Why is he sad?

10. What did Lila teach Dandelion that made him feel happy?

Coming soon!

Lila and
the Stinkbug

Visit us at www.thelilabooks.com
and follow us on Facebook.

Carl is a good friend of Lila. Carl is sight-impaired, but his nose works really well! (That's Carl taking his medicine on the page in this book where Lila explains how dandelions help the world!) While on a walk with Lila and Dandelion, Carl and his super-smeller nose come across a bug with a problem. Esby is a stinkbug whose stinker is stuck! How did this happen? How can the problem be fixed?!? Lila, Dandelion, Carl, and Esby work together to find a cure. *Lila and the Stinkbug* will help your child learn about consequences and why it's important to be kind to others.

Watch for the heartwarming, comical story of Lila and the Stinkbug to be released in the near future!

Draw yourself as a flower

Draw things you find where you live